Getting to Sleep

written by **Rozanne Lanczak Williams**
illustrated by **Ken Spengler**

Harcourt

Orlando   Boston   Dallas   Chicago   San Diego

www.harcourtschool.com

"It is nine o'clock
and I can't get to sleep."

2

Mom says, "Try counting some cows and some sheep."

3

"I'll help!" says a cow.
"I know how to do it."

"First, make a ten.
There's nothing to it."

7

"I'll add 1 more—me!
Wow! How many then?"

9

"5 white sheep, 5 black sheep.
That makes a ten."

10